Renew by phone
0845 0020 777
www.bristol-c...

eg Cabot is the author of the phenomenally
ccessful The Princess Diaries series. With vast
imbers of copies sold around the world, the
oks have topped the US and UK bestseller lists
weeks and won several awards. Two movies
sed on the series have been massively popular
oughout the world.

g is also the author of the bestselling *All
rican Girl*, *All American Girl: Ready or Not*, *Teen
l*, *Avalon High*, *How to be Popular*, *Nicola and the
ount*, *Victoria and the Rogue* and The Mediator
es, as well as several other books for teenagers
d adults. She lives in Florida with her husband
a her one-eyed cat, Henrietta.

Visit Meg Cabot's website at
www.megcabot.co.uk

Bristol Library Service

AN 3032509 9

Books by Meg Cabot

The Princess Diaries*
The Princess Diaries: Take Two*
The Princess Diaries: Third Time Lucky*
The Princess Diaries: Mia Goes Fourth*
The Princess Diaries: Give Me Five*
The Princess Diaries: Sixsational*
The Princess Diaries: Seventh Heaven*
The Princess Diaries: After Eight*

The Princess Diaries In Love
The Princess Diaries Guide to Life
The Princess Diaries Princess Files
The Princess Diaries Guide to Christmas
The Princess Diaries Yearbook 2007

All American Girl*
All American Girl: Ready or Not*

Avalon High*
Teen Idol*
How to Be Popular*
Nicola and the Viscount*
Victoria and the Rogue*

The Mediator: Love You to Death
The Mediator: High Stakes
The Mediator: Mean Spirits
The Mediator: Young Blood
The Mediator: Grave Doubts*
The Mediator: Heaven Sent

Look out for

The Princess Diaries: To the Nines
Jinx
Tommy Sullivan Is a Freak

For older readers

The Guy Next Door
Boy Meets Girl
Every Boy's Got One
Queen of Babble
Size 12 Is Not Fat
Size 14 Is Not Fat Either

* Also available in audio

AVALON HIGH
THE MERLIN PROPHECY

Created and written by

MEG CABOT

Illustrated by Jinky Coronado

HL
9/07

BRISTOL CITY COUNCIL
LIBRARY SERVICES
WITHDRAWN AND OFFERED FOR SALE
SOLD AS SEEN

MACMILLAN

TOKYOPOP

First published in the USA 2007 by HarperCollins Children's Books, a division of HarperColins Publishers

First published in the UK 2007 by Macmillan Children's Books
a division of Macmillan Publishers Limited
20 New Wharf Road, London N1 9RR
Basingstoke and Oxford
www.panmacmillan.com

Associated companies throughout the world

Acknowledgements
Many, many thanks to Jinky Coronado, Laura Langlie, Amanda Maciel, Julie Taylor
and the entire team at TOKYOPOP.

Associate Editor Kathy Schilling; *Lettering* Lucas Rivera; *Editor* Julie Taylor;
Digital Imaging Manager Chris Buford; *Pre-Production Supervisor* Erika Terriquez;
Art Director Anne Marie Horne; *Production Manager* Elisabeth Brizzi; *Managing Editor* Vy Nguyen;
VP of Production Ron Klamert; *Editor-in-Chief* Rob Tokar; *Publisher* Mike Kiley;
President and C.O.O. John Parker; *C.E.O and Chief Creative Officer* Stuart Levy

A **TOKYOPOP** Manga
TOKYOPOP and are trademarks or registered trademarks of TOKYOPOP Inc.
TOKYOPOP Inc.
5900 Wilshire Blvd. Suite 2000, Los Angeles, CA 90036, USA

Email: info@TOKYOPOP.com
Come visit us online at www.TOKYOPOP.com

ISBN: 978-0-330-45316-5

Text copyright © Meg Cabot LLC 2007
Illustrations copyright © TOKYOPOP Inc and HarperCollins Publishers 2007

The right of Meg Cabot and Jinky Coronado to be identified as the author and illustrator of this work
has been asserted by them in accordance with the Copyright, Designs and Patents Act 1988.

All rights reserved. No part of this publication may be
reproduced, stored in or introduced into a retrieval system, or
transmitted, in any form or by any means (electronic, mechanical,
photocopying, recording or otherwise), without the prior written
permission of the publisher. Any person who does any unauthorized
act in relation to this publication may be liable to criminal
prosecution and civil claims for damages.

1 3 5 7 9 8 6 4 2

A CIP catalogue record for this book is available from the British Library.

Printed and bound in Great Britain by Mackays of Chatham plc, Kent

This book is sold subject to the condition that it shall not,
by way of trade or otherwise, be lent, resold, hired out,
or otherwise circulated without the publisher's prior consent
in any form of binding or cover other than that in which
it is published and without a similar condition including this
condition being imposed on the subsequent purchaser.

For Benjamin

BRISTOL CITY LIBRARIES	
AN3032509 9	
PE	21-Aug-07
JF	£4.99

CHAPTER ONE

ONE SMALL BAND OF LOYAL SUPPORTERS-- THE ORDER OF THE BEAR--BELIEVED THAT THIS KING--THE NOBLE ARTHUR--WOULD RISE AGAIN, TO LEAD OUR WORLD FROM THE DARKNESS INTO THE LIGHT.

FOR NEARLY FIFTEEN HUNDRED YEARS,

THESE BELIEVERS HAVE WAITED,

ONLY TO SEE THEIR HOPES DASHED AGAIN...

...AND AGAIN.

BASICALLY, THE ORDER OF THE BEAR IS MADE UP OF A BUNCH OF HISTORIANS AND SCHOLARS WHO HAVE HELD ON TO THE BELIEF THAT ARTHUR WOULD SOMEDAY BE REINCARNATED...

...AND LEAD THE WORLD INTO A NEW AGE OF PEACE AND ENLIGHTENMENT, LIKE THE ONE THAT OCCURRED BACK WHEN CAMELOT EXISTED.

14

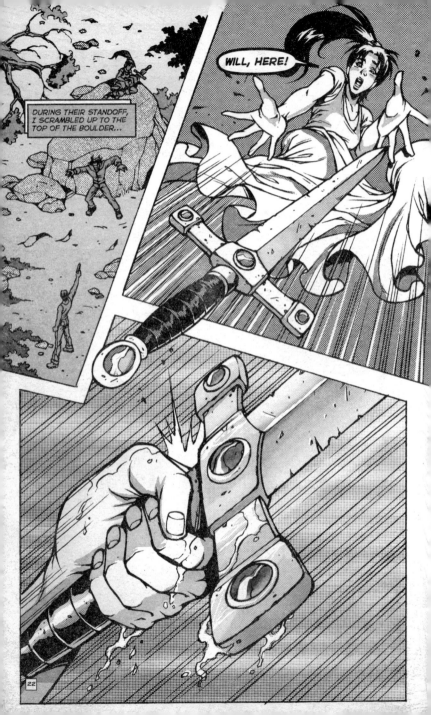

I HONESTLY DON'T KNOW HOW MUCH OF THAT IS TRUE. BUT I DO KNOW HOW LUCKY I AM. I MEAN, IS THERE ANY OTHER HIGH SCHOOL GIRL YOU KNOW WHO BASICALLY GETS TO LIVE WITH--EVEN IF IT'S ONLY PLATONICALLY...MUCH TO MY EVERLASTING CHAGRIN, WILL BEING TOO NOBLE TO MAKE A MOVE ON THE DAUGHTER OF THE PEOPLE WHO SO KINDLY TOOK HIM IN WHEN HIS OWN PARENTS THREW HIM OUT-- HER BOYFRIEND AND POSSIBLE REINCARNATION OF KING ARTHUR?

GOOD NIGHT.

G'NIGHT, YOU TWO.

RUFF!

GOOD NIGHT.

27

CHAPTER TWO

ESPECIALLY SINCE MARCO IS SAFELY LOCKED AWAY IN A PRIVATE MENTAL HOSPITAL AT HIS PARENTS' EXPENSE. AS WILL OFTEN POINTS OUT TO ME.

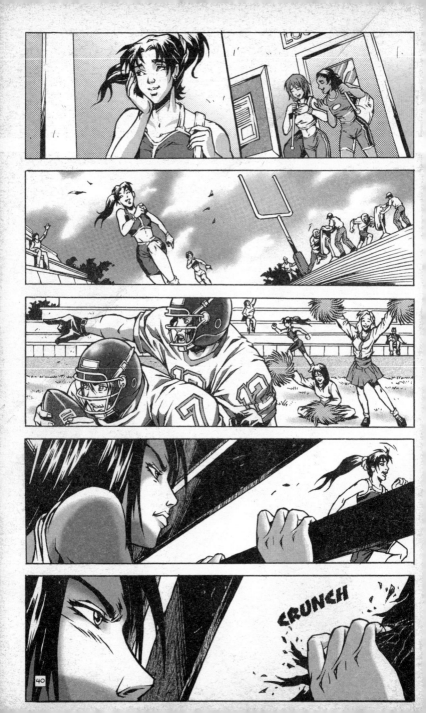

CRUNCH

I DON'T KNOW WHY I LET THEM TALK ME INTO GOING THROUGH IT. IT'S NOT LIKE I DON'T HAVE OTHER STUFF TO WORRY ABOUT...

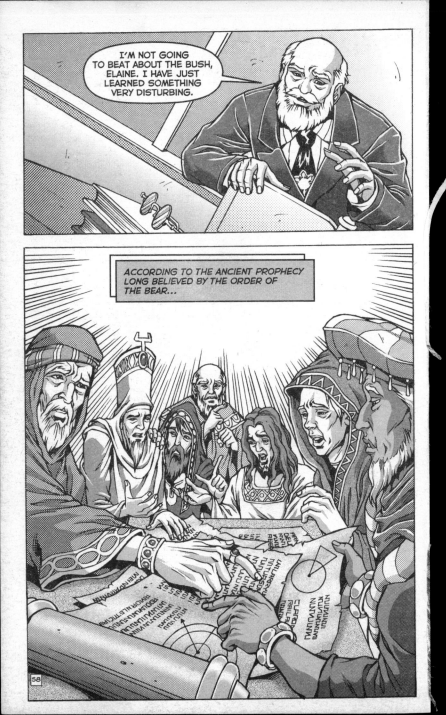

BUT I THOUGHT WE'D ALREADY DEFEATED THE DARK SIDE WHEN MARCO GOT ARRESTED--

SO DID I. BUT APPARENTLY PREVENTING MARCO FROM KILLING WILL WASN'T ENOUGH...JUST LIKE OUR BELIEVING IN WILL IS NOT ENOUGH.

HE'S GOT TO BELIEVE IN HIMSELF. HE'S GOT TO BELIEVE HE'S TRULY A KING.

BUT, MR M-- THIS IS SO NEVER GOING TO HAPPEN. I MEAN, WILL IS NO MORE LIKELY TO BELIEVE IN SOME ANCIENT PROPHECY ABOUT HIM BEING A REINCARNATED KING THAN I'M LIKELY TO...

...WELL, BE CROWNED HOMECOMING QUEEN!

AND HOW CAN I GET
WILL TO DO THE SAME?

CHAPTER THREE

WOW, YOU'RE REALLY TAKING THIS DRESS SHOPPING THING SERIOUSLY.

YOU HAVEN'T SAID A WORD IN TEN MINUTES.

SORRY, I WAS JUST THINKING ABOUT SOMETHING ELSE.

JUST WAIT.

WHY DO I FEEL SCARED NOW?

CHAPTER FOUR

...WITH NO KOOKY PROPHECIES I DON'T BELIEVE IN--

Avalon High

MEG CABOT

Avalon High, Ellie's new school, is pretty much what she'd expected. There's Lance, the hunky footballer; Jennifer, the cute cheerleader, Marco, the troublemaker. And then there's Will – the most gorgeous guy Ellie's ever met. She can hardly believe he likes HER.

When Will says he thinks he's met Ellie before, things start getting a little weird. A feeling that grows as Ellie discovers the strange bonds that entwine Will, Lance, Jen, Marco – and herself.

As darkness turns to danger, can Ellie stop the horrific chain of events that threatens to engulf them all . . . ?